Fables and Legends

by Barbara Gregorich

TEACHER'S GUIDE AND ANSWERS

This book teaches students the characteristics of various types of fables and legends. It also focuses on such literary elements as conflict, theme, character, irony, foreshadowing, and more. The challenging activities test students' understanding of entertaining stories from around the world. The teacher's guide (pages ii–iv) contains ideas for additional activities that provide reinforcement and extension of the concepts taught on the worksheets.

Answers

Page 1

1. Yes. Students' definitions will vary but should indicate that prose is the everyday form of speech or writing.
2. Answers may vary. Students may note that the characters in "The Hungry Elephant" are animals and the characters in "The Nut and the Wall" are inanimate objects.
3. b, a
4. Answer will vary but students should be able to support their answers.
5. Fables will vary. You may wish to review the characteristics of a fable described in the paragraph on this worksheet.

Extension Activity: Have students write an animal fable to illustrate the moral "Haste makes waste."

Page 2

1. He does not know that the dog has frightened away robbers on the first night.
2. That he now understands that it is more important to let the master sleep than it is to scare off robbers.
3. Answers will vary. The general thrust of answers should be that some people—especially when they do not have the facts—can never be pleased.
4. He did not realize that the bird helped the crocodile.
5. He smiled partly because he had fooled the fish, and partly because he knew the answer to the question but would not tell a foolish fish.
6. Some people are like crocodiles—they do not harm those who help them, but they harm others.
7. Both fables end without a summary or moral. They end on an inconclusive note, forcing the reader to think about the meaning.

Extension Activity: Have each student write the name of an interesting animal on a small piece of paper. Place the papers in a box. Have each student write a fable about the animal he or she chooses from the box. The fables should have a plot as well as a second level of meaning.

Page 3

1. The conflict is the struggle to eat and to not be eaten.
2. The antagonists are the owl and the lemming.
3. No.
4. The owl's goal is to eat the lemming. The lemming's goal is to not be eaten by the owl.
5. The conflict is the struggle to win the race.
6. The antagonists are the hummingbird and the heron.
7. Yes.
8. The goal is to win the race by reaching the western waters first.

Extension Activity: Ask students to identify a conflict in their lives or in society today. Have them write a fable that tells about the conflict. The fable should contain a "solution" to the conflict and a moral.

Page 4

Fables will vary. Check to see that all students incorporate the basic elements of a fable.

Page 5

1. d   2. c   3. a   4. e   5. b
6. Answers will vary. We are better off not delaying gratification until we are too old to truly enjoy it.
7. Students' fables will vary.

Page 7

1. He wants to please them.
2. He has no hair.
3. She is a complainer and is so tired that she calls for the ultimate end to all work.
4. No. When faced with the reality of Death, she prefers her hard work.
5. He never spends his money and enjoys the things money can buy.
6. She spills it because she is daydreaming about things she does not have.
7. "The Man with Two Wives"—too eager to please
   "The Old Woman and Death"— exaggerates
   "The Man and His Money"—enjoys hoarding
   "The Milkmaid and the Pail"—daydreams
8. D—"The Man with Two Wives"
   A—"The Old Woman and Death"
   C—"The Man and His Money"
   B—"The Milkmaid and the Pail"

Extension Activity: Read proverbs from a book of proverbs. Have students choose one proverb and work together to write a fable illustrating that proverb.

Page 9
1. the wolf
2. The wolf is a hypocrite. He is a thief who pretends to be honest. He is always hungry, but he is not willing to give up his freedom for food. He can be outsmarted by the clever fox and overpowered by the stronger lion.
3. "The Wolf and the Lion" and "The Wolf at Death's Door"
4. "The Wolf and the Dog" He makes a wise decision.
5. "The Wolf, the Fox, and the Well" The fox convinces the wolf there is cheese in the well.
6. Answers will vary but should indicate that some things are more important than being fed regularly.
7. Answers will vary but should indicate that one should beware of free offers that seem too good to be true.
8. Answers will vary but should indicate that even a thief feels indignant when robbed of his stolen goods and is quick to react like an honest person.
9. Answer will vary but should indicate that one should not be a hypocrite.
10. The content is the plot and the characters. The purpose is the moral.

Extension Activity: Have students write their ideas about the difference between a legend and a fable. Have students check the accuracy of these ideas when they learn about legends on the following pages.

Page 10
1. Calamity Jane
2. Robin Hood
3. Thor
4. Flying Dutchman
5. Davy Crockett
6. Pecos Bill
7. King Arthur
8. John Henry
9. Neptune
10. Johnny Appleseed

Extension Activity: Have students rank the legendary characters listed on the worksheet, putting the historical ones at the top, the ones that are possibly historical in the middle, and the purely mythical ones at the bottom. Discuss this ranking. In preparation for the following pages, discuss what constitutes myth and what constitutes history.

Page 11
1. They are parts of myths because they explain events such as how the earth was formed and from where the first god came.
2. They both begin with the time when the universe was empty and try to explain how things began. They are also similar in tone.
3. "The Earth Magician" refers to dry, sandy earth; it originated with a people from a dry region of the world. The ice in "The First God" indicates that the myth originated in northern lands.
4. the creation of Earth
5. the coming of the first god
6. Possible answers include how the sun, moon, stars, humans, and animals were created.

Page 12
1. He may have become king of England at a young age. He was king of England. He may have defended England against Saxon invaders.
2. The sword part of the story is probably invented or exaggerated.
3. Answers will vary but may indicate that it is highly unlikely that a young man could pull out the sword when many other stronger people had failed.
4. There may have been a Robin Hood. Robin Hood may have been the Earl of Huntingdon. He may have lived in Sherwood Forest with other men. They may have held games or celebrations.
5. Shooting an arrow through an arrow in flight is probably an exaggeration. The shooting of arrows through thin weed stalks and the wrestling events are probably exaggerations.
6. Answers will vary.

Extension Activity: Have students look up historical evidence about King Arthur in encyclopedias, history books, magazines, and other sources. Ask each student to write a brief report on what historians think Arthur did and how they think he lived. Compare the facts to the legends. (He wasn't really a king, but a Welsh warrior who fought the English.)

Page 13
1. & 2. Rinaldo, husband of Charlemagne's sister Aya, fought with the king in many battles. Rinaldo rode into battle on his famous horse, Bayard. Originally this huge horse lived in a thick forest ruled by a magician. The horse attacked all who came to ride it, for it knew that if it were knocked to the ground it would lose its angry strength. One night Rinaldo entered the forest. From a thicket, he heard a sudden noise. It was Bayard! The horse charged at the intruder, screaming and rearing. It kicked the sword from Rinaldo's hand, but when the horse reared to strike again, its hoof became stuck in a tree branch. Rinaldo rushed to the horse and pushed it to the ground. Its anger was gone and it was tame. Thus did Rinaldo come to own the greatest horse in the kingdom.

While Charlemagne and Rinaldo were fighting in Hungary, Agramante, king of Africa, was planning a treacherous attack on France. Agramante was being aided by Rodomonte, the fiery king of Algiers. "For the plan of attack to succeed," said Agramante, "we must have Rogero with our army." Rogero was being held prisoner by a magician in a fortress far away, so Agramante and Rodomonte asked a dwarf for help. The dwarf, Brunello, was the most clever thief in all of Africa. First, Brunello stole a magic ring which made the wearer invisible. Wearing the ring, Brunello was able to help Rogero escape from prison. Then Agramante, Rodomonte, and Rogero sailed toward France with 100,000 soldiers. Charlemagne had been warned and took his army back to France to await the attackers.

3. They both contain magicians and magic.
4. People in the period during which these were written believed in magic and magicians.
5. You could tell by the belief in magic and by the fact that the men rode into battle on horses.

Page 14
1. Students should underline "Usadagawa was said to be the greatest wrestler in the land."
2. Students should draw a wavy line under "...she held a large, heavy brazier..." or "Lifting the brazier in one hand..."
3. Students should draw two lines under "When he returns, the load of wood on his back will be so large it will block out the sun."
4. Answers will vary.
5. Students should underline "Niemonen said he would carry the rock by himself if the villagers would do what he told them."
6. rascal
7. Answers will vary.

Extension Activity: Many Japanese legends tell of mighty wrestlers, and many tell of rogues, knaves, and rascals. Select one such legend and read it to students. Ask them to compare Japanese legends to American legends that they know. What are the similarities? What are the differences?

Page 15
1. The Long-Ears   2. The Short-Ears
3. Yes. Justification will vary.
4. Answers may vary.
5. Answers will vary, but may include the fact that it is ironic that the Long-Ears died in their own trap. It is also ironic that a Long-Ear caused their deaths.

Extension Activity: Discuss why the legend would be less interesting if it did not contain irony. How would it be different if the Short-Ears had dug the pit?

Page 16
1. no
2. The narrator could easily continue telling about Davy's first year or some other episode.
3. Answers will vary.
4. The exaggeration about the size and strength of the baby makes it humorous.
5. Answers will vary, but students should be able to support their answers.

Extension Activity: Have students write a personal tall tale using events from their childhood as starters. From there they can add exaggeration. Ask students to explain the difference between boasting and exaggeration.

Page 19
The following answers to questions 1–12 are suggested answers only. Students should be able to support their answers.

1. f, j   2. h, i   3. b   4. c   5. h, i
6. g   7. e   8. a   9. j   10. d
11. i   12. d, j

13. Rascals: Niemonen, monks, stranger, possibly Niemonen's wife
Fools: city people, miller, men of Gotham, possibly miller's wife
14. Answers will vary. Some find it funny for someone to profit from another's foolishness. Some might think that rascals couldn't be rascals if people were not so foolish.
15. A robber would have simply wanted money. The stranger had two motives—fooling the fools and getting their money.

Page 20
1. foreshadow   2. character
3. fables   4. conflict
5. motive   6. historical
7. moral   8. fiction
9. dishonest   10. tall
11. exaggeration   12. antagonists
13. legends   14. irony
15. judgement   16. myths

iv

The Fable

A fable is a very short fictional tale that can be told in prose or in verse. In many fables, the main characters are animals or inanimate objects such as pitchers or chairs. Humans and gods can also be characters in a fable. The main purpose of a fable is to illustrate a moral, or lesson. Sometimes the moral is stated at the end of the fable. The moral of a fable can usually be summarized in a short saying or sentence.

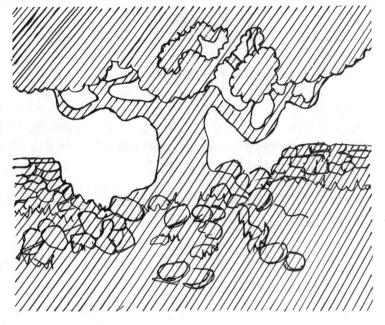

Read the two fables, then answer the questions below.

The Hungry Elephant

Once there was an elephant who was quite hungry. He found a swamp full of bamboo palms and, standing in the water, he tore down a palm. At the end of a branch was a tender leaf bud. As the elephant reached for the tasty bud with the tip of his trunk, the bud fell into the water. The elephant swished his trunk through the water, searching for the bud. This movement caused the water to become cloudy, and the elephant could not see the bud. Suddenly, a frog spoke. "Listen!" said the frog. "Listen!" The elephant stopped to listen. As everything became still, the water cleared and the elephant was able to see the bud clearly. He picked it up and ate it.

The Nut and the Wall

One day a crow with a nut in its beak flew over the countryside. The bird accidentally dropped the nut, which fell to the ground alongside a stone wall. "Oh, help me!" pleaded the nut to the wall. "I was taken from the tree and nearly eaten. Now I lie here far from home. All I ask for is a small hole in which I may die in peace."

The wall felt sorry for the nut and directed it to a little hole in the ground. The grateful nut rolled into the hole. A few days later the nut burst open, sending up shoots and sending down roots. Higher and higher climbed the plant, deeper and deeper went the roots, pushing at the wall, causing parts of it to topple. Too late, the wall cried out, "Oh, what have I done? I have allowed the nut to destroy me!"

1. Are both stories told in prose? _____ Use your own words to define the term *prose*.

_____

_____

2. How are the characters in "The Hungry Elephant" different from the characters in "The Nut and the Wall"? _____

_____

3. Match each fable with its moral.

_____ "The Hungry Elephant"   a. Consider the consequences before you act.

_____ "The Nut and the Wall"   b. You can't solve a problem until you calm down and observe what's around you.

4. Which character(s) in these fables could be described as clever? _____

Write adjectives to describe each of the other characters. _____

_____

5. Write a fable with the same moral as one of the fables on this page. Create different characters in a different setting.

Animal Fables

Since a fable is an indirect means of telling a truth about life or about people, it usually contains two levels of meaning. On the first, or more obvious level, it is a simple story about animals, people, or things. A certain action takes place, and there is a beginning, middle, and end. The author has another purpose and this is the second level of meaning. The author uses the elements of the story to say something that is broader, or more meaningful, than the story itself. This is the moral, or truth, that hides under the simple surface of the fable.

THE WATCHDOG

A rich man had a dog which he chained at night outside his house. One dark night, robbers came to the house. As they began to climb over the outside wall, the dog started to bark. He barked so loudly that the robbers ran away, but he also woke up his master. "Why did you wake me up?" shouted the man, as he cuffed the poor dog on the ear.

"Aha!" thought the dog to himself. So the next night the dog slept very soundly, so soundly in fact that the same robbers came over the wall and made off with all the rich man's money.

In the morning, the man shouted angrily at the dog, "Why didn't you wake me up, you foolish dog?"

"Alas," thought the dog to himself, as the man once again cuffed him on the ear.

THE CROCODILE, THE BIRD, AND THE FISH

A fish was amazed to see a bird fly into the mouth of a crocodile. While the bird picked out some of the bugs that were biting the inside of the crocodile's mouth, the huge beast remained quiet. The bird flew away when it was finished. "That looks like fun," said the fish.

"Would you like to try?" asked the crocodile in a soft voice. The fish swam into the crocodile's mouth and was swallowed immediately.

"Why me and not the bird?" the fish cried out as it disappeared down the crocodile's throat. The crocodile smiled and, well fed, swam to the shore to lie in the sun.

Read the two fables above and answer the questions about them.

1. In the first fable, what does the man not know?

_____

2. When the dog says "Aha," what do you think he is telling himself? _____

_____

3. How would you summarize the first fable's second level of meaning? _____

_____

4. What did the fish not understand about the bird's relationship to the crocodile? _____

_____

5. Why do you think the crocodile smiled? _____

6. How would you summarize the second level of meaning in the crocodile fable? _____

_____

7. What is it about the endings of the two fables that might make a reader look for a second level of meaning? _____

_____

Animal Fables

In each fable, there is a conflict. A conflict is a struggle, usually between two characters or forces. When two characters are in conflict, they are called antagonists. Sometimes antagonists have the same goal, but each wants to be first to complete it or wants to be better at it.

Read the two fables below, then answer the questions.

THE LEMMING AND THE OWL: One fine Arctic day, Lemming was sitting and eating outside his burrow. Lemming was not paying attention to the sky, and down swooped Owl, settling between Lemming and his burrow. "I see two dog teams coming this way," announced Owl. "They will tear you to pieces."

Lemming pretended to be frightened. "Oh no, Owl! Please eat me yourself so that I will not be torn to pieces by the dog teams!"

"Excellent idea," replied Owl.

"First," said Lemming, "let me entertain you before dinner. I will sing and you may dance."

"Excellent idea," said Owl, who began to dance to Lemming's song. While Owl danced, Lemming ran past him and slipped into his burrow. "Come out," coaxed Owl. "It is safe now. The dog teams are gone."

Lemming simply laughed at Owl and stayed safely in his burrow.

1. What is the conflict? _____

_____

2. Who are the antagonists? _____

3. Does each antagonist have the same goal? _____

4. Describe the goal or goals. _____

_____

THE HERON AND THE HUMMINGBIRD: Hummingbird wanted to race Heron from the eastern waters to the western waters. Heron did not want to race, but Hummingbird pestered her so much that finally Heron agreed. The two birds took off and in three seconds Hummingbird was out of sight. Heron flapped along slowly but steadily. At the end of the day, while Hummingbird rested, Heron passed her. The next morning, Hummingbird started out again and passed Heron at noon. Again Hummingbird had to rest at night and Heron passed her. The third day of the race, Hummingbird did not pass Heron until late in the afternoon. That night Hummingbird again rested while Heron kept on flapping. Heron reached the western waters early in the morning, but Hummingbird did not get there until late in the evening. "How did you do it?" demanded Hummingbird. "I'm so fast I can fly circles around you! How did you do it?"

5. What is the conflict? _____

_____

6. Who are the antagonists? _____

7. Does each antagonist have the same goal? _____

8. Describe the goal or goals. _____

_____

Animal Fables

The cartoon panels above show two animal characters in conflict. Think about the conflict and the goal of each animal. What happens? How and why? Write an _original_ fable about this situation. Call it "The Rabbit and the Porcupine." End your fable with a moral.

_____

_____

_____

_____

_____

_____

_____

_____

_____

_____

_____

_____

_____

_____

Animal Fables

Sometimes the moral of a fable concerns social or political problems or institutions. That is, the fable is commenting about some social belief or law or accepted way of doing things. In such fables, the characters often stand for figures such as kings, peasants, governments, or taxes.

Read the fable below, then answer the questions.

THE SQUIRREL AND THE LION: A squirrel decided that, unlike his fellow squirrels, he would work for the lion, who was rich and strong. So while the other squirrels chattered, climbed trees, and stored nuts for the winter, this squirrel worked for the lion. The lion promised to give the squirrel a wagonful of nuts for his work. Winter came, but the lion did not pay. Of course, the squirrel dared not demand payment from a lion, so, envying his fellow squirrels, the squirrel went on working for the lion. After many years, the squirrel was too old to work. The lion then kept his promise and gave the squirrel a wagonful of nuts—hazelnuts, walnuts, hickory nuts, almonds—beautiful and delicious nuts of every kind. Nowhere did any squirrel have such a perfect hoard of nuts, but the squirrel had a problem: he had long ago lost all his teeth.

In questions 1-5, draw a line from each statement to the word or phrase that best completes it.

1. The squirrel probably stands for a(n)

2. The lion probably stands for a(n)

3. The wagonful of nuts probably stands for

4. The lost teeth might stand for lost

5. The fable might be about

a. money or good things in life

b. pensions

c. employer or government

d. worker

e. youth

6. In your own words, explain what social issue you think the writer of the fable is trying to write about and what his point is. _____

_____

_____

_____

_____

7. The writer of the fable is looking at the negative or bad side of this social issue. Turn this paper over and rewrite the fable so that it shows the positive side of the social issue.

People Fables

Motive and character are closely related in a fable. Since fables tend to be simple stories, the characters they portray tend to be simplified, too. Fables often deal with such character types as "the rich person," "the foolish person," or "the coward." How do we recognize these characters? We identify character types by analyzing the characters' motives, or reasons for action. For example, a person who always does things in order to make money could be identified as "the greedy person."

After reading the four fables on pages 6 and 7, answer the questions.

THE MAN WITH TWO WIVES

Long ago, a man had two wives whom he wanted very much to please. One of his wives was older than he, and one was younger. At this time, it so happened that gray hairs began to appear among the brown hairs on the man's head. The younger wife, seeing the gray hairs, said to her husband, "Surely you don't want any gray hairs, do you?"

"Of course not," the man answered, wanting to please his wife. So day after day, the young wife began to pluck out his gray hairs.

The old wife was delighted to see the gray hairs. "You look so good in gray!" she cried. "Why not let me pull out these ugly brown hairs?"

"Of course, dear," said the man, still wanting to please. So from that day forward, the old wife began to pluck the brown hairs from the man's head. This went on for many months until one day the man looked in a mirror. He blinked and looked again. The he shouted to his two wives, "Alas, look at me now! Look at what you have done!"

THE OLD WOMAN AND DEATH

An old woman worked very hard all day long. Day after day she collected wood for the fire, cooked, sewed, and even milked the cows. At the end of a particular day, during which she had worked especially hard, the woman was carrying wood into the house from the woodpile. She groaned under the heavy load. As she entered the house, she suddenly muttered aloud, "Ah, I'm so worn out that I wish Death would come this very instant and take me away." At that moment, she heard a soft knock at the open door and turned to see an ugly bony creature smiling at her. It was Death himself!

"Did you want something?" Death asked.

"Uh—uh—uh," the old woman stammered. Then she swallowed and said, "Yes, please help me carry these heavy pieces of wood over to the fireplace."

People Fables, cont.

THE MAN AND HIS MONEY

There was once a rich man who took pride in his money. To avoid theft, he buried it in the backyard of his house. Each week he would dig up the money and gaze happily at all that he owned. Then, one day, a robber saw him digging up the money. When the man left his home, the robber dug up the money, took it, replaced the dirt, and fled. The next week, the man went to look at the money. When he discovered that it was gone, he cried out. A neighbor, hearing his cries, came to his aid. The rich man told his neighbor that the money had been stolen. The neighbor thought for a moment and then asked, "What did you do with your money?"

"Nothing," the man answered, "I only liked to look at it."

"Well," said the neighbor, "why not go on looking at the empty hole? It will do you just as much good!"

THE MILKMAID AND THE PAIL

A milkmaid was carrying milk to the marketplace. As was the custom in those time, she carried the milk in a pail which she balanced on her head. While she walked, she thought, "I will sell my milk for good money, and with that money I will buy a chicken. From that chicken will come other chickens, and those chickens will lay many eggs. I will sell the eggs, and with that money I will buy a bright red scarf. I will wear the scarf on my head. My friends will be very jealous, but I won't care!" She laughed to herself. "I will merely strut past them and shake my head like this—" As she shook her head, the pail of milk clattered to the ground, spilling all its contents. The poor milkmaid had to go home empty-handed.

1. Why does the man in "The Man with Two Wives" allow each wife to pull out his hair?

_____

2. What happens to the man at the end of the story? _____

3. In "The Old Woman and Death," what is the woman's motive for crying out for Death?

_____

4. Does she really want Death to come? _____ Support your answer._____

_____

5. In "The Man and His Money," what does the man never do with his money?

_____

6. Why does the milkmaid spill her milk? _____

_____

7. Match each fable with the character type it contains by drawing a line from the fable to the description.

_____ "The Man with Two Wives"	One who exaggerates
_____ "The Old Woman and Death"	One who daydreams too much
_____ "The Man and His Money"	One who is too eager to please
_____ "The Milkmaid and the Pail"	One who enjoys hoarding things

8. Next to each title in question 7, write the letter of the moral that best suits the fable.

A. Be careful what you wish for. B. Don't count your chickens before they hatch.
C. What isn't used may as well not exist. D. If you give in to everyone, you may end up with nothing to give.

Comparing Fables

Most fables are thousands of years old. They come from all parts of the world. Fables from many different countries have certain similarities. This is because people and animals share certain character traits regardless of culture. Fables have content. Content is who the characters are and what the plot is—what happens in the story. Fables also have a purpose. The purpose is the moral—the lesson that they teach.

Read the fables below, then answer the questions on page 9.

THE WOLF AND THE DOG: A thin, hungry wolf noticed a fat, sleek dog walking around a house. "Tell me," said the wolf, "why are you so fat and sleek? How do you get enough to eat?"

"I am fed by my master," replied the dog. "I keep thieves away from this house, and he feeds me every day." The wolf asked if he could help the dog guard the house. The dog agreed and the two began their watch.

As the two walked along, the wolf noticed a white ring where the fur was missing around the dog's neck. "Why is your neck rubbed raw?" asked the wolf.

"That is where my master ties an iron collar around my neck every day," said the dog. "At night he unties me so that I can guard the house."

"Some things are more important than being fed regularly," said the wolf, turning away.

THE WOLF AT DEATH'S DOOR: Once there was a dying wolf. He began to think back on his life. "I have been a sinner, but not a complete sinner," he explained to Fox. "Why, I remember a time when a little lamb walked by me. It was so close that I could have snapped it in two with my jaws, but I did not. No, I let the little lamb go."

The fox had been listening to the wolf's dying argument. "Yes," said the fox, "I remember the time well. You were chocking on a bone that was stuck in your throat."

THE WOLF AND THE LION: A wolf had stolen a sheep and was carrying it home to eat it when a lioness happened by. The lioness, bigger and stronger, took the sheep from the wolf. "Thief! Robber!" cried the wolf. "You are not fair! You took my property!"

"Ah," said the lioness, smacking her lips as she settled down to eat. "That is too bad. Especially since you doubtlessly came by it honestly."

THE WOLF, THE FOX, AND THE WELL: One evening a fox strolled by a well. Looking down, he saw the round moon reflected in the well. Thinking that the reflection was a piece of cheese, the fox jumped into the bucket at the top of the well and rode it down to the bottom of the well. He soon realized his mistake: there was no way to get out of the well unless somebody rode down in the other bucket which was now at the top of the well. The fox waited and waited.

The next evening a wolf strolled by and looked into the well. "Ummm," said the fox. "Look what I have found down here, Brother Wolf, a splendid round of delicious cheese. There is enough for two. Why don't you ride down in the bucket I've left up there for you?" The wolf leaped into the bucket and rode it down, causing the fox's bucket to go to the top. The fox then jumped out of the bucket and strolled away.

Comparing Fables, cont.

The questions below are based on the fables on page 8. Write the answer to each question.

1. Which animal appears in all four fables?_____

2. Describe the character traits of this animal. What is he like? _____

   _____

   _____

3. In which two fables does the wolf appear as a hypocrite (a person who says one thing but does

   the opposite)?_____

4. In which fable does the wolf appear to have the best character traits?_____

   Why? _____

   _____

5. In which fable is the wolf outsmarted? _____

   How?_____

   _____

6. What is the moral of "The Wolf and the Dog"? _____

   _____

   _____

7. What is the moral of "The Wolf, the Fox, and the Well"?_____

   _____

   _____

8. What is the moral of "The Wolf and the Lion"? _____

   _____

   _____

9. What is the moral of "The Wolf at Death's Door"? _____

   _____

   _____

10. What is the difference between the content and the purpose of a fable? _____

    _____

    _____

The Legend

A legend is a story that usually has some basis in fact, but contains exaggeration, or stretching of the truth. Sometimes there is little exaggeration, sometimes there is much. Legends are usually stories of folk heroes, or of how natural things such as the sun, the oceans, or earthquakes came to be. Each nation has its own legends. Paul Bunyan is an example of an American legend. There was probably once a real lumberjack who was very big and very strong. His name may even have been Paul Bunyan. Then people began to exaggerate stories about Paul and Babe, his blue ox. Thus Paul Bunyan became a legend. Legends fall into one of two large categories. Mythical legends are closest to pure invention. Historical legends are closest to pure fact.

For each description below, fill in the name of the correct legendary character.

Thor	Flying Dutchman	King Arthur	Davy Crockett	Calamity Jane
Robin Hood	John Henry	Pecos Bill	Johnny Appleseed	Neptune

1. _____ was an American frontierswoman who wore men's clothes. She said she had been a scout for General Custer, had ridden with the Pony Express, and could hit any target with a gun.

2. _____ was an English outlaw who lived in Sherwood Forest. He robbed from the rich to give to the poor.

3. _____ is a god in Scandinavian myths. He is the god of thunder, war, and strength.

4. The _____ was the name of a ship and the captain who was condemned to sail it for all time. It was a ghost ship and its crew were dead men. Sailors claim to see this ship sailing across the top of the water, like a ghost.

5. _____ was an American folk hero born in Tennessee. He told funny frontier stories. He was elected to Congress and later he went west and died fighting at the Alamo.

6. _____ was a cowboy who formed the Grand Canyon while digging for gold and dug out the Rio Grande during a drought.

7. _____ lived in England long ago, according to legend, and fought with the Knights of the Round Table.

8. _____ was a Black American folk hero who worked on the railroad driving steel into the tracks. He challenged a steam drill to a race, driving steel through a mountain.

9. In Roman mythology, _____ was the god of the sea.

10. John Chapman was the real name of _____, an American pioneer who planted apple trees from Massachusetts to Ohio.

Mythical Legends

Myths are stories that were first told orally, before people could write or read. Myths tell about gods and super heroes and the universe. They explain how the world or the forces in it came to be. At one time, myths were the basis of the religions of many people around the world. Myths were an explanation of the causes of natural events. Today we read and enjoy myths because of their imaginative power, but long ago they expressed people's view of the world.

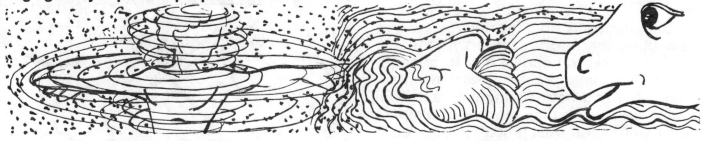

THE EARTH MAGICIAN

Everything was darkness. There was neither sun nor stars nor moon nor Earth. Slowly the darkness swirled around itself, deeper and deeper, faster and faster. Darkness into darkness into darkness, until out of the darkness came Earth Magician.

Earth Magician drifted alone in the great darkness. "Oh, I wish to cease this drifting," he said to himself. And lo, with a magic stick he took a speck of dust from his chest and rolled it into a ball. Then he patted the ball until it became flatter and wider. Now he could stand on the dry desert place. He danced in the sandy dark. He had created the world.

THE FIRST GOD

In the beginning the world was a thick fog curling over a great expanse of ice. Ice was everywhere and under the ice, fires burned, which were guarded by Surtr. He was called the Flame Giant because of his fiery sword. One day, a spark from Surtr's sword melted a bit of the ice, and as the ice melted it turned into strange new shapes. It became Ymir, the Frost Giant, and his cow Audhumla, the giver of life. Audhumla licked the ice and suddenly a head appeared. A huge figure was buried in the ice! It was Bure, the first of the gods!

Read the two selections above and then write the answers to the questions.

1. Why are these two selections parts of myths rather than mere stories? _____
_____

2. What do these two selections have in common? Explain. _____
_____

3. What minor details in each myth might give you clues about from which part of the world the
   myth maker came? _____
_____

4. What big event does "The Earth Magician" explain? _____

5. What main event does "The First God" explain? _____

6. If the rest of the myth "The Earth Magician" were told, what other things might it explain? _____
_____

11

Historical Legends

Many legends are rooted in history. After the deaths of famous men or women, stories are told about them. As time passes, these stories are expanded until facts become mixed with imaginary deeds and events. It is sometimes difficult to distinguish truth from invention. One can speculate that story events which seem unlikely, based on normal human strength or abilities, have probably been invented. Historians can help distinguish fact from fiction by studying the records of the past and reporting on what probably occurred.

Below are two historical legends. Read them and then write the answers to the questions.

HOW ARTHUR BECAME KING: The sword, Excalibur, was set in a huge stone by the magician, Merlin. "Only the true king of England can remove this sword," he had said solemnly. Many lords and knights tried to pull out the sword, but it remained in place. One day young Arthur passed the rock while seeking a sword for a friend. Arthur was unaware of his royal blood because he had not been raised at court. His father, the king, had died and the people of England were anxiously awaiting a successor. Arthur gripped the handle of the sword and was amazed as it slid easily from the stone. The people nearby gathered around him and cheered. Here at last was the true king of England. Arthur was crowned king and defended England from the Saxon invaders for many years.

THE FEAST IN THE FOREST: Robin Hood's merry band, having captured the evil Sheriff of Nottingham and taken his gold, held a great feast. Tomorrow they would give the gold to the poor, but today, deep in Sherwood Forest, they played at games. Some chased the king's deer, dragging them down by their antlers; others shot arrows through thin weed stalks at one hundred paces. Robin Hood, who was secretly the Earl of Huntingdon, shot an arrow through an arrow while it was in flight! Later, Little John wrestled a wild boar! Then, as darkness approached, the band ate, drank ale, and told stories until they fell asleep under the stars.

1. What two events in the Arthur legend might be based on historical fact? _____

_____

2. What big event in the story is probably an invention or an exaggeration? _____

_____

3. What makes you think so? _____

_____

4. List two events in the Robin Hood legend that might be based on historical fact. _____

_____

5. List one event in the legend that is probably an invention or an exaggeration. _____

_____

6. Turn the paper over and continue the Robin Hood legend, beginning with what happened the next day. Add one event that could be historical and one that is most likely an exaggeration.

French Legend

Charlemagne (Charles the Great) was a famous ruler of the Middle Ages. He lived from 742 to 814 A.D. Charlemagne was King of the Franks, the ancestors of the present-day French people. His courts in Paris and elsewhere attracted many knights, scholars, poets, and adventurers. After his death, people told stories about him. These legends of Charlemagne are now a part of French folk stories. They contain some historical truth, but they also contain inventions and exaggerations. Thus they mix fact and fiction. Fact is something that really happened. Fiction is invention.

Read the two legends below, then write the answers to the questions.

HOW RINALDO CAME TO POSSESS BAYARD

Rinaldo, husband of Charlemagne's sister Aya, fought with the king in many battles. Rinaldo rode into battle on his famous horse, Bayard. Originally this huge horse lived in a thick forest ruled by a magician. The horse attacked all who came to ride it, for it knew that if it were knocked to the ground it would lose its angry strength. One night Rinaldo entered the forest. From a thicket, he heard a sudden noise. It was Bayard! The horse charged at the intruder, screaming and rearing. It kicked the sword from Rinaldo's hand, but when the horse reared to strike again, its hoof became stuck in a tree branch. Rinaldo rushed to the horse and pushed it to the ground. Its anger was gone and it was tame. Thus did Rinaldo come to own the greatest horse in the kingdom.

THE INVASION OF FRANCE

While Charlemagne and Rinaldo were fighting in Hungary, Agramante, king of Africa, was planning a treacherous attack on France. Agramante was being aided by Rodomonte, the fiery king of Algiers. "For the plan of attack to succeed," said Agramante, "we must have Rogero with our army." Rogero was being held prisoner by a magician in a fortress far away, so Agramante and Rodomonte asked a dwarf for help. The dwarf, Brunello, was the most clever thief in all of Africa. First, Brunello stole a magic ring which made the wearer invisible. Wearing the ring, Brunello was able to help Rogero escape from prison. Then Agramante, Rodomonte, and Rogero sailed toward France with 100,000 soldiers. Charlemagne had been warned and took his army back to France to await the attackers.

1. In both legends, underline each sentence or phrase that is probably based on historical fact.

2. In both legends, put a wavy line under sentences or phrases that are no doubt fiction, or inventions of the imagination.

3. What fiction or invention do the two stories have in common? _____

_____

4. Why do you think this is so? _____

_____

5. If you did not know when Charlemagne lived, how could you tell by these stories that he lived many years ago? _____

_____

_____

Japanese Legend

In many types of stories, authors foreshadow events. To foreshadow is to hint at or suggest what will happen later in the story. Something that is said or done prepares you for a what will happen. The two stories below are legends from Japan. Each of them involves foreshadowing.

Read the stories, then follow the directions and answer the questions.

THE MIGHTY WRESTLER: Usodagawa was said to be the greatest wrestler in the land. Once a famous wrestler went to challenge him. When the wrestler arrived at Usodagawa's home, he met Usodagawa's mother. In her hands she held a large, heavy brazier, a metal pan in which burning coals are held. Lifting the brazier in one hand, she pointed toward the mountains. "Usodagawa is gathering firewood," she said, setting the brazier down. "When he returns, the load of wood on his back will be so large it will block out the sun." Then she went away. While the famous wrestler waited for Usodagawa's return, he tried to lift the brazier but could not move it.

When Usodagawa returned at noon, the land grew dark. As he took the load of wood off his back, the light returned. The famous wrestler challenged Usodagawa. As the two men wrestled, Usodagawa grabbed the famous wrestler and lifted him high in the air. "Heaven or Earth?" Usodagawa asked him.

"Earth!" answered the famous wrestler, and he was thrown to the ground. When the famous wrestler went home, he prayed that never again might there be another wrestler such as Usodagawa.

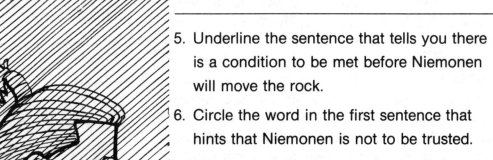

NIEMONEN AND THE ROCK: Niemonen was a country rascal. In his village there was a rock so huge that 20 men could not lift or carry it. Niemonen said he would carry the rock by himself if the villagers would do what he told them. They agreed. Niemonen told them to tie a thick rope around the rock. They did. Then he grabbed one end of the rope and said to the 20 men, "Now raise this rock." They tried, but could not. Niemonen threw down the rope in disgust. "If you don't do what I tell you, I will not carry the rock for you!"

1. Underline the first sentence that tells you that Usodagawa is a good wrestler.

2. Put a wavy line under what the mother *does* that hints at how strong her son might be.

3. Draw two lines under what the mother *says* that hints at how strong her son might be.

4. At which point in the story do you suspect that the famous wrestler will not win?

_____

_____

5. Underline the sentence that tells you there is a condition to be met before Niemonen will move the rock.

6. Circle the word in the first sentence that hints that Niemonen is not to be trusted.

7. Turn this paper over and rewrite "The Mighty Wrestler" so that the famous wrestler wins. Use forshadowing to hint at how your story will end.

14

Polynesian Legend

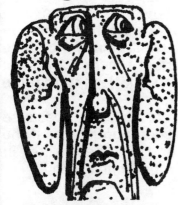

Many works of literature, including legends, contain irony. Irony refers to an outcome that is the opposite of what is expected. If a murderer intends to poison someone, but accidentally poisons himself, the situation is ironic—it is the opposite of what the murderer intended.

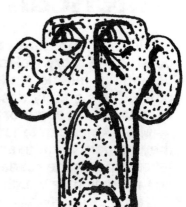

The legend below comes from Easter Island, a South Pacific island 2,000 miles west of South America. When it was first visited by Europeans in 1722, it was filled with giant stone statues, many of them weighing 50 tons. The human-looking statues had long ears and wore crowns.

Read the legend, and then answer the questions.

THE LONG-EARS AND THE SHORT-EARS: The Long-Ear people came to the island first. They put heavy pieces of jewelry in their ears to stretch them. That is how they came to be Long-Ear people. They lived on the best land and ruled the island.

The Short-Ear people came much later. They did not have hanging ears. They were forced to live on the poorest land which was covered with rocks.

One day the Long-Ears told the Short-Ears to remove the rocks from Short-Ear land. The Short-Ears refused. They believed that if they moved the rocks, the land would be improved and the Long-Ears would seize it. The Long-Ears became angry at the refusal. They dug a long, long pit and placed a tremendous amount of firewood inside it.

A Short-Ear woman and a Long-Ear man who were married fought continuously. One day when the husband was especially angry at his wife, he shouted, "The pit is being dug for all of the Short-Ears!"

The Short-Ear woman hurried to her people and told them what her husband had said. The Short-Ears were afraid when they heard about the Long-Ears' plan. A meeting was called, and the Short-Ears decided on a course of action. During the night they hid near the pit. In the morning, when the Long-Ears arrived at the pit, the Short-Ears surrounded them. The Short-Ears used spears to force the Long-Ears into the pit. They lit the firewood and that was the end of the Long-Ears.

1. Who held the power on the island? _____

2. Who had the worst land?_____

3. Do you think the Short-Ears' fears were justified? _____ Why or why not? _____

    _____

4. Who would you expect to win a battle between these two groups? _____

    Why? _____

5. What is the irony in the story? _____

    _____

    _____

American Legend

Most legends are considered to be tales. A tale is a story told by a narrator, a person outside the story. Tales are different from short stories. Short stories usually have a definite beginning, middle, and end. They also contain a climax, where the action reaches a critical point. Tales simply describe a series of events. A reader sometimes gets the feeling that the narrator could add more incidents at any time.

Most American legends are tales, and many are tall tales. Tall tales are called tall because they contain huge exaggerations. The exaggerations are always described seriously, as if the teller expects the reader to believe them. Tall tales are also humorous and are often written in an informal style which incorporates the dialect, or speech patterns, of a particular area.

Read the tall tale below, then answer the questions.

DAVY CROCKETT: Folks all know that this here feller, Davy Crockett, was some great hunter and some great leader who died at the Alamo. That's not even the half of it! Heavens to Betsy, no sir! Davy was a whale of a great baby, too. Just you listen to this. Davy was born in the great state of Tennessee, near the Nolachucky River. Was the baby big? Hey, Davy's first cradle was twelve feet long! For a pillow the little ripsnorter had a wildcat's skin filled with the down of more than thirty geese and ten ganders. Truth is, Davy couldn't even stay in the cabin, because if he laughed out loud the barrels tipped in the cellar. Bear meat, my friends, and buffalo milk were Davy's diet. But all that's nothing. You should have been there the day he floated down the river, all the way down he did, just paddling with an old spoon. Folks cheered that one, I'll tell you, just as they'd be cheering for Davy his whole life!

1. Does this tale have a definite end or conclusion? _____

2. Explain your answer. _____

_____

3. Give two examples of the informal language that is found in this tale. _____

_____

_____

4. What makes this tall tale humorous? _____

_____

5. List three examples of exaggeration found in this tall tale. _____

_____

_____

American Legend

The story of Johnny Appleseed, whose real name was John Chapman, is an American legend. He lived from 1774 to 1845. He spent most of his adult life traveling through the country giving apple seeds to settlers.

In the spaces below, write two different stories about Johnny Appleseed. Make A a serious legend. Make B a tall tale. The cartoons above may help you write about Johnny Appleseed's deeds.

A: LEGEND _____

_____

_____

_____

_____

_____

_____

_____

_____

_____

_____

_____

_____

_____

_____

_____

_____

_____

B: TALL TALE _____

_____

_____

_____

_____

_____

_____

_____

_____

_____

_____

_____

_____

_____

_____

_____

_____

_____

Comparing Legends

People around the world have many legends about rascals and fools. Rascals are people who are dishonest jokers. Fools are people who lack common sense.
Read the three legends and answer the questions on page 19.

NIEMONEN AND THE FIRE: One day Niemonen left his country home and traveled to the city, which was a long distance from his home. While walking down the street, he stopped suddenly and shouted, "My house is on fire!" People stared at him. He told them where he lived and they looked where he was pointing, but they could see nothing at that great distance. They told him he could not possibly see his house burning, but he insisted he could. Niemonen bet them five hundred gold pieces that his house was burning. Bets were placed. A few days later, a messenger arrived from the country. He reported that Niemonen's house had burned down, but his wife was safe. The house had burned on the exact day and at the exact hour Niemonen had stopped and shouted. Of course it had for he had ordered his wife to burn down their house on that day at that hour!

THE DONKEY MONK: A miller owned a donkey. Every night he left it tied outdoors on a long rope. One night some monks were out thieving. They spied the donkey and took it. One of the monks stayed at the mill and tied the rope around his neck. When the miller awoke, he was astonished. "Who are you?" the miller demanded.

"I was your donkey," answered the monk. "I sinned, and I was punished by being turned into a donkey. I have now paid for my sins and have been turned back into a monk." So the miller let the monk go.

A few days later the monks took the donkey to a fair to sell it. They hoped to get a good price for the beast they had stolen. It just so happened that the miller and his wife were at the same fair. They saw the donkey. "Look!" said the miller. "The monk has sinned again." The miller and his wife told everyone the story of the donkey and the monk. Naturally, no one would buy the donkey because everyone believed it would soon turn back into a monk. The thieves were stuck with the donkey.

THE TWELFTH MAN: One day twelve men of Gotham went fishing. Some stood in the water; some stood on dry land. At the end of the day, they set out for home. "I hope no one was drowned," said one.

"Let us count," said another. So each man of Gotham counted, and each counted only eleven for no man thought to count himself.

"By heavens, one of us was drowned!" they cried. They went back to the water and thrashed about, weeping and wailing. Soon a stranger came by and asked what was the matter. They told him that twelve of them had gone fishing and one was missing

"Hmmm," said the stranger. "What will you give me if I find the twelfth man?" They promised to give him all their gold. The stranger took a stick and hit each man on the shoulder as he counted. "One! Two!..." And indeed he counted twelve, so they gave the stranger all their gold and thanked him again and again for finding the twelfth man. The twelve men went home happy, and the stranger went home rich.

          FABLES AND LEGENDS

Comparing Legends

The questions below are based on the legends on page 18. Write the letter or letters of the correct answer(s). Some answers might be used more than once.

_____ 1. Such a person lacks judgement or common sense.

_____ 2. These fools believed the monk.

_____ 3. This rascal fooled the city people.

_____ 4. Such a person is a joker and dishonest.

_____ 5. These fools actually upset the plans of the rascals.

_____ 6. This woman helped a rascal.

_____ 7. This rascal took advantage of twelve fools.

_____ 8. This rascal lied to the miller.

_____ 9. These fools could not count.

_____ 10. These fools believed a man could see what they couldn't see.

_____ 11. This woman believed what the rascal told her husband.

_____ 12. These fools lost their money.

a. monk

b. Niemonen

c. rascal

d. city people

e. stranger

f. fool

g. Niemonen's wife

h. miller

i. miller's wife

j. men of Gotham

13. *In the space below, write the names of all the characters in the three tales. Classify each character as a rascal or a fool.*

Rascals	Fools

14. Readers of legends usually like rascals because there is something appealing about rascals. Why do you think this is so? _____

_____

_____

15. What is the difference between the stranger and a robber who might come upon the men of Gotham and steal their money at the point of a sword? _____

_____

_____

Review

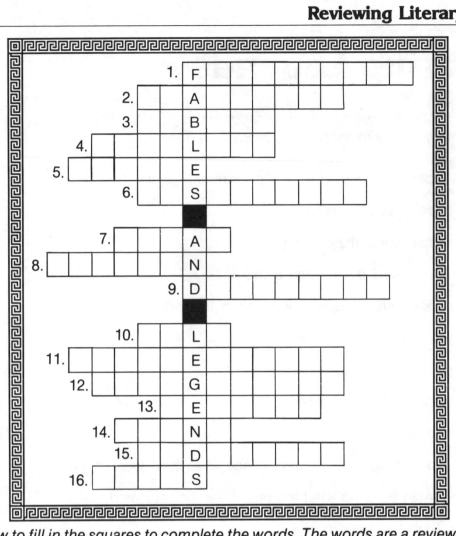

Use the clues below to fill in the squares to complete the words. The words are a review of terms used in the lessons on fables and legends.

1. To hint at or suggest something that will happen later in a story is to _____.
2. If you label a person as greedy, hasty, or dull-witted, you are talking about the person's _____.
3. Short stories in which the characters are usually animals are _____.
4. A struggle between two characters or forces is _____.
5. The reason a person does what he or she does is called a _____.
6. This type of legend has its roots in history.
7. This is the lesson or purpose of a fable.
8. This type of writing is invention, not fact.
9. A rascal is a joker who is _____.
10. Many American legends are this type of tale.
11. The stretching of the truth is _____.
12. Two characters in conflict are _____.
13. Stories about King Arthur, Charlemagne, and Robin Hood are _____.
14. When the opposite of what is intended or expected happens, it is called _____.
15. A fool lacks good _____.
16. Stories about super heroes, gods, and the universe that were told before people could read or write are _____.